Ladybird Readers

What Is It?

To access the audio and digital versions
of this book:

1 Go to www.ladybirdeducation.co.uk
2 Click "Unlock book"
3 Enter the code below

3uzFVNWmvj

Notes to teachers, parents, and carers

The *Ladybird Readers* Beginner level helps young language learners to become familiar with key conversational phrases in English. The language introduced has clear real-life applications, giving children the tools to hold their first conversations in English.

This book focuses on introducing various animals in English, as well as practicing the question "What is it?".

There are some activities to do in this book. They will help children practice these skills:

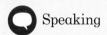 Speaking  Listening* 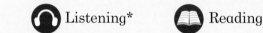 Reading

*To complete these activities, listen to the audio downloads available at www.ladybirdeducation.co.uk

Series Editor: Sorrel Pitts
Chants by Sorrel Pitts

LADYBIRD BOOKS

UK | USA | Canada | Ireland | Australia
India | New Zealand | South Africa

Ladybird Books is part of the Penguin Random House group of companies
whose addresses can be found at global.penguinrandomhouse.com.
www.penguin.co.uk   www.puffin.co.uk   www.ladybird.co.uk

Penguin
Random House
UK

Text inspired by *"Slowly, Slowly, Slowly," said the Sloth* by Eric Carle, first published in Great Britain by Puffin Books, 2002
This version first published by Ladybird Books 2024
001

Printed in China

The authorized representative in the EEA is Penguin Random House Ireland, Morrison Chambers, 32 Nassau Street, Dublin D02 YH68

A CIP catalogue record for this book is available from the British Library

ISBN: 978–0–241–58778–2

All correspondence to:
Ladybird Books
Penguin Random House Children's
One Embassy Gardens, 8 Viaduct Gardens, London SW11 7BW

MIX
Paper | Supporting
responsible forestry
FSC
www.fsc.org
FSC® C018179

What Is It?

Inspired by
"Slowly, Slowly, Slowly," said the Sloth
by Eric Carle

"What is it?"
says the sloth.

It is a puma! Hello, Puma!

"What is it?"
says the sloth.

It is a frog. Hello, Frog!

"What is it?"
says the sloth.

It is a monkey. Hello, Monkey!

"What is it?"
says the sloth.

It is a turtle. Hello, Turtle!

"What is it?"
says the sloth.

It is a jaguar. Hello, Jaguar!

Your turn!

1 Listen. Circle the words.

1  turtle ⟨jaguar⟩

2  sloth puma

3  turtle monkey

4 sloth frog

2 Read the sentences. Match.

1 It is a monkey.

2 It is a puma.

3 It is a frog.

4 It is a turtle.

3 Read and clap!

What is it?
It is a puma. Hello, Puma!

What is it?
It is a frog. Hello, Frog!

What is it?
It is a monkey! Hello, Monkey!

What is it?
It is a turtle. Hello, Turtle!

Hello, animals! How do you do?
What animal are you?